11+
Verbal Activity
Standard 20 Minute Tests

TESTBOOK **1**

Dr Stephen C Curran

Edited by Andrea Richardson

Sub-editor: Nell Bond

This book belongs to

Accelerated Education Publications Ltd.

Verbal Activity Test 1

Rearrange these words into proper sentences.

e.g. diet important is a balanced
   <u>A balanced diet is important.</u>

1) toilet where the is?   _____

2) pounds costs it four   _____

3) your change clothes into best   _____

Work out which codes belong with which words and then answer the questions.

MAN	RAN	ARE	RAM
512	156	517	712

e.g. What is **ARE** in code? <u>156</u>

Write the following words in code:

4) **MAN** _____   5) **RAM** _____   6) **RAN** _____

Choose one word from the brackets that answers each question.

e.g. Which of these words means 'present'?
   (away, absent, here, where)   <u>here</u>

7) Which of these words means 'material used to mend a hole'?
   (pit, patch, pith, pitch)   _____

8) Which of these words means 'pleased'?
   (glad, please, sad, glade)   _____

9) Which of these words means 'frown'?
   (crown, nasty, scowl, shout)   _____

Underline the word in the brackets that will complete the analogy.

e.g. **Plane** is to **air** as **boat** is to (land, <u>water</u>, pilot)

10) **Beef** is to **meat** as **tuna** is to (animal, fish, bird)

11) **Down** is to **up** as **fall** is to (drop, slide, rise)

12) **Pig** is to **sty** as **horse** is to (stable, field, kennel)

Underline the word that cannot be made by using the letters of the word in capitals.

e.g. **POSTER**	rope	stop	rest	<u>star</u>	pore
13) **HEART**	tar	had	tea	hate	the
14) **PARCEL**	lap	ale	can	are	carp
15) **PINES**	snip	sins	pens	nips	pies

Underline the two words that begin and end with the same letter.

e.g. rate	<u>seems</u>	step	<u>level</u>	mare
16) boots	shoes	trainers	sandals	clogs
17) edge	start	rear	toys	each
18) treat	code	reach	lame	else

Read the following statements and answer the questions.

Paul and John like cricket. Balraj and Colin like swimming. Colin and Paul like rounders. Paul and Balraj like karate.
(Clue: use the table to help you)

Name	Cr	Sw	R	K
Paul				
John				
Balraj				
Colin				

e.g. Who likes swimming and karate? __Balraj__

19) Who likes cricket and rounders? _____

20) Who only likes one sport? _____

Score [ ]   Percentage [ ] %

Verbal Activity Test 2

Work out what each letter is in code then find the missing word.

e.g. If **old** is written as **753**, which word is written as **3755**? _doll_

1) If **tale** is written as **4327**, which word is **2347**? _____

2) If **meat** is written as **2941**, which word is **2419**? _____

3) If **tide** is written as **1832**, which word is **2381**? _____

Remove one letter from the word in capitals to make a new word. Use the clue to help you.

e.g. **BLACK**   the opposite of front   _back_

4) **TRAIL**   trains use these   _____

5) **PAINT**   when something hurts   _____

6) **HAUNT**   meat eating animals do this   _____

Underline the two words that are made from the same letters.

e.g.	toe	end	eat	den	ten
7)	tan	ran	and	tar	ant
8)	pit	top	pat	ton	tap
9)	bit	nib	bun	bin	nab

Write the next word in this pattern of words.

e.g.	fan, fun	ran, run	ban, _bun_
10)	toe, to	sob, so	got, _____
11)	bat, bet	mat, met	vat, _____
12)	pot, put	got, gut	rot, _____

© 2011 Stephen Curran

Write true or false against each of these sentences.

e.g. Some cars are red. _true_

13) July comes before June. _____

14) There are always thirty one days in a month. _____

15) There are fourteen days in a fortnight. _____

Underline the two words in each line that are spelt differently but sound the same.

e.g.	toy	<u>two</u>	toe	tie	<u>too</u>
16)	blue	bowl	bawl	ball	blow
17)	their	they	these	those	there
18)	soul	sail	sane	sale	sold

Some children took a spelling test. They were given marks out of 10. Adam gained 1 more mark than Deborah. Bobby lost 3 marks. Carla achieved full marks. Eric had 1 mark less than Bobby. Deborah got 4 marks less than Bobby.

_____

_____   Use this chart to place the

_____   children in mark order.

_____

_____

Now answer these questions:

e.g. Who achieved 6 out of 10? _Eric_

19) Who was second in the test? _____

20) What was the lowest score achieved? _____

Score [ ] **Percentage** [ ] %

A B C D E F G H I J K L M N O P Q R S T U V W X Y Z

Verbal Activity Test 3

The following questions involve looking for letters in words.

e.g. Which letter occurs twice in **tainted**? <u>t</u>

1) What letter is in **book** but not in **robin**? _____

2) Which letter occurs three times in **themselves**? _____

3) Which letter is in **spade** and also in **donor**? _____

Underline the word in the brackets so the sentence makes sense.

e.g. A cow produces (eggs, bacon, <u>milk</u>, grass).

4) All months have (years, days, decades, holidays).

5) A fox lives in a (nest, sty, den, sett).

6) All dogs have (puppies, paws, fleas, collars).

Rewrite these jumbled letters as proper words.

e.g. tves <u>vest</u>

7) jnesa _____

8) telb _____

9) tirsh _____

(Clue: they are
all items of clothing)

Write these words in their correct alphabetical order.

e.g. tea   juice   coffee   chocolate   smoothie
    <u>chocolate</u>   <u>coffee</u>   <u>juice</u>   <u>smoothie</u>   <u>tea</u>

10) coach   moped   lorry   bus   car

    _____   _____   _____   _____   _____

A B C D E F G H I J K L M N O P Q R S T U V W X Y Z

11) football   rounders   netball   cricket   tennis

_____   _____   _____   _____   _____

12) lounge   kitchen   bedroom   hall   loft

_____   _____   _____   _____   _____

Add one letter to the word in capitals to make a new word. Use the clue to help you.

e.g. **LOW**   not fast   _SLOW_

13) **AND**   a part of your body   _____

14) **RED**   we learn to do this at school   _____

15) **RAG**   to pull something along   _____

Underline the word that cannot be made by using the letters of the word in capitals.

e.g. **POSTER**   rope   stop   rest   <u>star</u>   pore

16) **TRAMPLE**   team   ramp   pear   leap   plan

17) **PLANETS**   nest   pane   tone   tape   stale

18) **CRATERS**   tear   rate   stare   term   care

Four children enjoy different sports.
Amar and Michael like football. Deena and Ella like hockey. Amar and Ella like tennis. Deena and Michael like volleyball.

(Clue: draw up a table)

Now answer these questions:

e.g. Who likes football and tennis?   _Amar_

19) Who enjoys hockey and volleyball?   _____

20) Who enjoys tennis, but not football?   _____

Score [ ]   **Percentage** [ ] %

Verbal Activity Test 4

Underline the word that has none of the same letters.

e.g.	boots	spots	<u>trial</u>	free	butter
1)	ginger	bells	trite	drops	boot
2)	singing	wrote	nine	freed	paper
3)	trees	greater	bottle	deter	later

Underline the word that when spelt backwards will make the given word.

e.g. (port, arts, <u>part</u>) is **trap** spelt backwards.

4) (bard, brad, drip) is **drab** spelt backwards.

5) (post, tops, stop) is **spot** spelt backwards.

6) (vile, live, veil) is **evil** spelt backwards.

Write the word that remains after the first and last letters of the given word have been removed.

e.g. plates ___late___

7) flowers _____

8) pleases _____

9) brains _____

Underline the two words that are most opposite in meaning.

e.g.	<u>tall</u>	small	<u>short</u>	tiny	fat
10)	away	far	gone	out	near
11)	sun	light	dim	glare	dark
12)	friend	love	bad	hate	fight

Rearrange these words into proper sentences.

e.g. diet important is a balanced
      <u>A balanced diet is important.</u>

13) book her read Prianka history

_____

14) shoes clean for your school

_____

15) up steep walked hill John the

_____

Underline the two words that are made from the same letters.

e.g. toe   <u>end</u>   eat   <u>den</u>   ten

16) ten   not   tan   net   tin

17) ran   rat   tap   run   tar

18) cot   out   act   cat   art

Work out the age of the person by using the information given.

e.g. Tom is half as old as Devraj.
      Tom is 12, how old is Devraj?   <u>24</u>

19) The ages of Billy and Raymond equal that of Ranila.
     If Ranila is 16 and Billy is 9, how old is Raymond? _____

20) In three years time Harry will be twice as old as I
     am now. If I am seven now, how old is Harry? _____

Score [   ] **Percentage** [   ] %

Verbal Activity Test 5

Underline the word in the brackets so the sentence makes sense.

e.g. A cow produces (eggs, bacon, <u>milk</u>, grass).

1) All babies have (bottles, prams, faces, nappies).

2) All motor vehicles use (diesel, fuel, petrol, kerosene).

3) All games have (bats, players, nets, balls).

Write the next letter or letters in the series.

e.g.	**AZ**	**BY**	**CX**	**DW**	<u>EV</u>
4)	**AB**	**DE**	**GH**	**JK**	_____
5)	**ZX**	**WU**	**TR**	**QO**	_____
6)	**AC**	**EG**	**IK**	**MO**	_____

Write the next word in this pattern of words.

e.g.	fan, fun	ran, run	ban, <u>bun</u>
7)	did, dud	mid, mud	bid, _____
8)	ban, bat	can, cat	fan, _____
9)	led, lead	red, read	bed, _____

Underline the word in the brackets that will complete the analogy.

e.g. **Plane** is to **air** as **boat** is to (land, <u>water</u>, pilot)

10) **Chirp** is to **bird** as **miaow** is to (dog, sheep, cat)

11) **Food** is to **eat** as **water** is to (river, drink, wash)

12) **August** is to **July** as **May** is to (June, March, April)

A B C D E F G H I J K L M N O P Q R S T U V W X Y Z

Underline the letters of the word that has been jumbled up and write the correct word in the space.

e.g. Trisha had no <u>nep</u> to write with.   _pen_

13) Paul put on his shoes and cosks for school.   _____

14) There was a beautiful red soer in the garden.   _____

15) "Hurry up," said Mum. "You're too owls."   _____

Underline the two words in each line that are spelt differently but sound the same.

e.g.	toy	<u>two</u>	toe	tie	<u>too</u>
16)	bear	bore	bar	bare	bow
17)	meant	meat	mate	moat	meet
18)	hole	heel	heal	hurl	hail

Read the following statements and then answer the questions.

Five children sat an English test. There were twenty questions. Carol got half her answers wrong. Gail made four mistakes. Simraj gained three more marks than Carol. Amar scored two marks less than Gail and Maria achieved two marks more than Simraj.

(Clue: draw up a table)

e.g. How many marks did Amar gain? _14 marks_

19) Who achieved the highest score? _____

20) Who scored the lowest? _____

Score ☐ Percentage ☐ %

ABCDEFGHIJKLMNOPQRSTUVWXYZ

Verbal Activity Test 6

Underline the two words that are made from the same letters.

e.g. toe   <u>end</u>   eat   <u>den</u>   ten

1) pop   sop   gas   sap   sag

2) ate   lap   tee   ale   tea

3) tow   tcn   two   wet   too

Underline the word in the brackets so the sentence makes sense.

e.g. A (dear, dare, dire, <u>deer</u>) is an animal.

4) A (pare, pier, pear, pair) is a fruit.

5) A (rein, rain, reign, ruin) is the strap of a bridle.

6) A (raid, read, ream, reed) is a water plant.

Study the words carefully and answer the questions.

apple   **peach**   **banana**   **pear**

e.g. What letter is in **pear** but not **peach**?   <u>r</u>

7) How many words have double letters?   _____

8) Which letter appears more than any other?   _____

9) Which letter in **apple** does not appear in **pear**?   _____

Underline the word that when spelt backwards will make the given word.

e.g. (port, arts, <u>part</u>) is **trap** spelt backwards.

10) (fowl, flow, bowl) is **wolf** spelt backwards.

11) (snap, saps, span) is **pans** spelt backwards.

12) (tars, stab, rats) is **star** spelt backwards.

A B C D E F G H I J K L M N O P Q R S T U V W X Y Z

Work out which codes belong with which words and then answer the questions.

TOO	TWO	WON	TO
634	53	533	563

Write the following words in code:

e.g. **TO** _634_ ~~53~~

13) **WON** _____

14) **TWO** _____

15) What is **5364** as a word? _____

The following questions involve looking for letters in words.

e.g. Which letter occurs twice in **tainted**?   _t_

16) Which letter is found once in **paint** but twice in **spanner**?   _____

17) Which letter is found three times in **excellent**?   _____

18) Which letter is in **stirs** but not in **rusts**?   _____

Work out the correct day by using the information given.

e.g. If the 3rd of May is a Wednesday, what day was the 30th of April?   ← go backwards   _Sunday_

(Use a calendar like this to help.)	**30th Apr**	1st May	2nd May	3rd May
	Sun	Mon	Tues	Wed

19) If the 4th of December is a Saturday, what day was the 29th of November?   _____

20) If the 29th of January is a Tuesday, what day will the 2nd of February be?   _____

Score ☐ Percentage ☐ %

13

Verbal Activity Test 7

Rewrite these jumbled letters as proper words.

e.g. malp   _palm_

1) koa   _____

2) chirb   _____

3) wye   _____

(Clue: they are all types of tree)

Remove one letter from the word in capitals to make a new word. Use the clue to help you.

e.g. **BLACK**   the opposite of front   _back_

4) **FOWL**   a bird of prey   _____

5) **VAIN**   a vehicle   _____

6) **CLUB**   a young lion   _____

Work out what each letter is in code then find the missing word.

e.g. If **old** is written as **753**, which word is written as **3755**? _doll_

7) If **2839** is **earn**, what will **9283** be?   _____

8) If **lamp** is written as **8167**, what will **718** be?   _____

9) If **5322** is **toss**, what will **2335** be?   _____

Underline the word in the brackets that will complete the analogy.

e.g. **Plane** is to **air** as **boat** is to (land, <u>water</u>, pilot)

10) **Sparrow** is to **bird** as **poodle** is to (cat, farm, dog)

11) **Long** is to **short** as **wide** is to (big, narrow, smart)

12) **Pen** is to **ink** as **pencil** is to (wood, sharpen, lead)

Write the next letter or letters in the series.

e.g.	**AZ**	**BY**	**CX**	**DW**	<u>EV</u>
13)	**A**	**C**	**F**	**J**	___
14)	**AZ**	**CX**	**EV**	**GT**	___
15)	**AB**	**ZY**	**CD**	**XW**	**EF**	___

Underline the two words in each line that are spelt differently but sound the same.

e.g.	toy	<u>two</u>	toe	tie	<u>too</u>
16)	hard	hear	hair	hay	here
17)	knew	know	now	new	nor
18)	bay	by	boy	be	buy

Read the following statements and then answer the questions.

Cynthia is taller than Eloise but not as tall as Balraj.
Adam is shorter than Eloise. David is taller than Balraj.

_____
_____
_____   Use this chart to place the
_____   children in size order.
_____

e.g. Who is the tallest? ___David___

19) Who is the shortest? _____

20) Who is in the middle, in terms of height, of the five?

_____

Score [ ] Percentage [ ] %

Verbal Activity Test 8

Rearrange these words into proper sentences.

e.g. diet important is a balanced

<u>A balanced diet is important.</u>

1) very home he arrived early

  _____

2) your where homework is school?

  _____

3) train the London took we to

  _____

Underline the word in the brackets so the sentence makes sense.

e.g. A cow produces (eggs, bacon, <u>milk</u>, grass).

4) All birds have (talons, plumage, fur, claws).

5) A badger usually lives in a (byre, kennel, sett, stable).

6) A calendar always has (dates, photographs, seconds, pictures).

The following questions involve looking for letters in words.

e.g. Which letter occurs twice in **tainted**? <u>t</u>

7) What letter is found twice in **educational**? _____

8) Which two letters in **dental** are also in **lions**? ___ and ___

9) Which letter is found three times in **sausages**? _____

Write the next word in this pattern of words.

e.g. fan, fun   ran, run   ban, _bun_

10) lot, lit   pot, pit   hot, _____

11) hoop, hop   flan, fan   loop, _____

12) tip, pit   pool, loop   live, _____

How many different letters are there in each of the following words?

e.g. banana   _3_

13) follow   ____

14) barrier ____

15) engineer ____

Rewrite these jumbled letters as proper words.

e.g. lpena   _plane_

16) rtma   _____   (Clue: they are
                                all forms of transport)
17) choac   _____

18) yrerf   _____

Work out the correct day by using the information given.

e.g. If the 3rd of May is a Wednesday, what
      day was the 30th of April?   ___Sunday___

(Use a calendar like this to help.)	**30th Apr**	1st May	2nd May	3rd May
	Sun	Mon	Tues	Wed

19) If the 1st of August is a Friday, what day
     was the 28th of July?   _____

20) If the 10th of March is a Tuesday, what
     day was the 3rd of March?   _____

Score [ ]   Percentage [ ] %

Verbal Activity Test 9

Underline the two words in each line that are spelt differently but sound the same.

e.g.	toy	<u>two</u>	toe	tie	<u>too</u>
1)	see	sow	sea	saw	say
2)	rays	rows	roars	rose	race
3)	sign	some	sun	sum	sin

Work out what each letter is in code then find the missing code or word.

e.g. If **old** is written as **753**, which word is written as **3755**? <u>doll</u>

4) If **read** is written as **2394**, how would you write **deer**? _____

5) If **fast** is written as **5384**, what will **84355** be? _____

6) If **trade** is written as **49213**, what will **9243** be? _____

Remove one letter from the word in capitals to make a new word. Use the clue to help you.

e.g.	**BLACK**	the opposite of front	<u>back</u>
7)	**THAT**	something you can wear	_____
8)	**TONE**	a heavy weight	_____
9)	**FLAN**	something used to cool yourself	_____

Underline the two words that are most similar in meaning.

e.g.	<u>new</u>	old	shiny	<u>fresh</u>	dead
10)	begin	go	end	start	delay
11)	ring	hit	play	pull	strike
12)	earth	plants	sea	land	air

A B C D E F G H I J K L M N O P Q R S T U V W X Y Z

Underline the word that has none of the same letters.

e.g.	boots	spots	<u>trial</u>	free	butter
13)	sales	peace	night	edge	dated
14)	baby	deed	bubble	tight	lame
15)	treat	worse	doctor	doom	reed

_____

Underline the two words that are most opposite in meaning.

e.g.	<u>tall</u>	small	<u>short</u>	tiny	fat
16)	open	down	enter	out	shut
17)	by	buy	bring	sell	give
18)	live	ill	die	sick	horse

_____

The chart shows how many newspapers were sold each day over a period of one week.

Monday	Tuesday	Wednesday	Thursday	Friday	Saturday
12	20	19	31	14	36

Answer these questions.

e.g. On which day were the fewest sold? <u>Monday</u>

19) How many fewer were sold on Friday than Thursday? _____

20) How many more were sold on Saturday than on Monday? _____

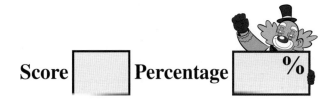

Score ☐ **Percentage** ☐ **%**

ae © 2011 Stephen Curran

Verbal Activity Test 10

Underline the word in the brackets so the sentence makes sense.

e.g. A cow produces (eggs, bacon, <u>milk</u>, grass).

1) A bird usually lives in a (burrow, nest, den, lair).

2) A book always has (pages, jokes, diagrams, sums).

3) Rain is always (heavy, cold, warm, wet).

Rearrange these words into proper sentences.

e.g. diet important is a balanced
<u>A balanced diet is important.</u>

4) to trees dangerous is climb it

_____

5) like Christmas receive children presents to

_____

6) holiday Spain we our in spent

_____

Write the next word in this pattern of words.

e.g. fan, fun   ran, run   ban, <u>bun</u>

7) hoop, hop   loop, lop   poop, _____

8) pan, pen   man, men   fan, _____

9) ball, bells   call, cells   tall, _____

The following questions involve looking for letters in words.

e.g. Which letter occurs twice in **tainted**?   <u>t</u>

10) Which two letters occur twice in **autumnal**?   ____ and____

ABCDEFGHIJKLMNOPQRSTUVWXYZ

11) Which letter occurs twice in **biscuit** but not in **trade**? _____

12) Which letter occurs three times in **registered**? _____

Underline the letters of the word that has been jumbled up and write the correct word in the space.

e.g. Trisha had no <u>nep</u> to write with. <u>pen</u>

13) psaws swarmed around their nest. _____

14) We went to the bank to get some shca. _____

15) The fche prepared the food in the restaurant. _____

Underline the two words that are most opposite in meaning.

e.g. <u>tall</u>   small   <u>short</u>   tiny   fat

16) right   write   odd   rite   wrong

17) fur   soft   stone   hard   rock

18) loud   music   quiet   quite   song

These are the marks that three children scored in two tests.

	Maths	Science
Priya	14	19
Peter	17	17
Naomi	19	16

Answer the following questions.

e.g. Who gained the same mark for both tests? <u>Peter</u>

19) Who achieved the highest total marks? _____

20) Who scored the lowest total marks? _____

Score [ ] Percentage [ ] %

Verbal Activity Test 11

Underline the two words that are made from the same letters.

e.g. toe   <u>end</u>   eat   <u>den</u>   ten

1) tub   bit   tab   but   bet

2) rum   ram   mum   arm   air

3) arc   con   cab   ark   car

Place the following words in alphabetical order by writing **1**, **2**, **3**, **4**, **5** in the brackets.

e.g. are (1) cat (3) day (4) elephant (5) bin (2)

4) oak (__) conifer (__) ash (__) willow (__) chestnut (__)

5) spoon (__) fork (__) teaspoon (__) tablespoon (__) knife(__)

6) London (__) Washington (__) Auckland (__)
   Berlin (__) Paris (__)

Underline the two words that are the odd ones out.

e.g. small   brief   <u>expand</u>   short   <u>big</u>

7) rose   tulip   stem   daffodil   nectar

8) cup   jug   mug   beaker   bowl

9) cottage   house   room   kitchen   flat

Underline the word in the brackets that will complete the analogy.

e.g. **Plane** is to **air** as **boat** is to (land, <u>water</u>, pilot)

10) **Snow** is to **white** as **sea** is to (black, blue, red)

11) **Bounce** is to **ball** as **skip** is to (rope, run, hop)

12) **Green** is to **go** as **red** is to (delay, stop, move)

Study how the second set of letters has been formed from the first, then repeat the process to find the answer. Use the alphabet above to help you.

e.g. **EP** is to **FQ** as **GR** is to <u>HS</u>

13) **B** is to **D** as **G** is to ____

14) **DC** is to **HG** as **QP** is to ____

15) **ZX** is to **WU** as **JH** is to ____

Underline the word in the brackets which is most opposite in meaning to the word in capital letters.

e.g. **RIGHT**   (true, <u>wrong</u>, correct, bad, real)

16) **TAME**   (angry, wild, free, fierce, scary)

17) **STRONG**   (feeble, build, failure, brave, muscle)

18) **LOST**   (search, lose, seek, hide, found)

Read the following statements and then answer the questions.

Jane and Sally like dogs. Roy and Meena like cats.
Meena and Jane like hamsters. Sally and Roy like rabbits.

(Clue: draw up a table)

e.g. Who likes cats and hamsters? <u>Meena</u>

19) Who likes dogs and hamsters? _____

20) Who likes rabbits and cats? _____

Score [ ] **Percentage** [ ] **%**

Verbal Activity Test 12

Rearrange the letters in capitals into a proper word so the sentence makes sense.

e.g. Our dog RAKBS loudly.   BARKS

1) John realised he had lost his KOBO.   _____

2) Laura went to school on her KEIB.   _____

3) Claire hung her coat on the OKHO.   _____

Choose the correct grouping for each of the words below. Write the group letter in the spaces provided.

A: Vegetables   B: Fruits   C: Meat

e.g. a) potato: _A_   b) pork: _C_

4)   a) veal: ____   b) kiwi: ____

5)   a) cherry: ____   b) turnip: ____

6)   a) leek: ____   b) beef: ____

Underline the word in the brackets which goes best with the words outside the brackets.

e.g. gerbil, mouse, hamster (badger, fox, rat, rabbit, beaver)

7) pigeon, robin, puffin   (wolf, cuckoo, squirrel, mole, cat)

8) board, dice, counters   (rules, run, floor, luck, compete)

9) page, story, words   (audio, chapter, poster, television, radio)

Underline the two words that need to change places in order for the sentence to make sense.

e.g. The mobile rang phone continuously.

10) Colin scored the final in the goal minute.

11) The guide harness wore a leather dog.

12) Naomi's cold tingled in the toes.

Underline the four-letter word that is hidden at the end of one word and the beginning of the next word and write it in the space provided. The order of the letters must not be changed.

e.g. My radio can b<u>e ver</u>y loud at times.   *ever*

13) Ravneet was playing in the park.   _____

14) We are going on holiday to Spain.   _____

15) Jim must be at football training on time.   _____

Underline one word from each set of brackets that go together to form a compound word. The word in the first set of brackets always comes first.

e.g. (sit, <u>man</u>, stand)   (now, <u>age</u>, past)

16) (sea, rain, sky)   (bird, gull, day)

17) (head, jaw, knee)   (bone, back, skin)

18) (ring, wrong, cross)   (out, day, roads)

Work out the correct day or date by using the information given.

e.g. If the 3rd of May is a Wednesday, what day was the 30th of April?   *Sunday*

(Use a calendar like this to help.)	**30th Apr**	1st May	2nd May	3rd May
	Sun	Mon	Tues	Wed

19) If the 1st of June is a Wednesday, what will the date be on the following Saturday?   _____

20) If the 2nd of December is a Tuesday, what day will it be on the 30th of November?   _____

Score [ ] **Percentage** [ ] **%**

Verbal Activity Test 13

Write the next word in this pattern of words.

e.g. fan, fun   ran, run   ban, _bun_

1) rat, rot   cat, cot   pat, _____

2) place, pace   black, back   sling, _____

3) ban, bane   wan, wane   man, _____

Write the letter that will end the first word and start the second word in the space provided.

e.g. DIS (_H_) OUR

4) NES (___) AME

5) SNA (___) ACK

6) PUL (___) ADY

If **RABBIT** is written in code as **342256**, find the following codes and words.

e.g. Find the code for **TAB**.   642

What word does **643** represent?   TAR

7) Find the code for **BAT**.   _____

8) What word does **2456** represent?   _____

9) Find the code for **BARB**.   _____

Remove one letter from the word in capitals to make a new word. Use the clue to help you.

e.g. **BLACK**   the opposite of front   _back_

10) **STAND**   we find this on a beach   _____

11) **BEAT**   you hit a ball with this   _____

12) **BLEAR**   a large animal   _____

Underline the word that has none of the same letters.

e.g. boots   spots   <u>trial</u>   free   butter

13) sheep   tents   metal   beech   luggage

14) floor   niece   apple   books   shelf

15) period   tablet   tight   grammar   rattle

Underline the word in the brackets so the sentence makes sense.

e.g. A cow produces (eggs, bacon, <u>milk</u>, grass).

16) A sandwich always has (salmon, ham, bread, butter, cheese).

17) A town always has (an airport, shops, a swimming pool, a river, a beach).

18) A tree always has (roots, fruits, berries, leaves, flowers).

Read the following statements and then answer the questions.

Gary is three years older than Cathy and currently twice as old as John. Cathy is one year older than John. John is 4 years old.

(Clue: use this diagram to help you)

Oldest   _____
2nd Oldest   _____
Youngest   _____

e.g. How old is Cathy?   _5_

19) How old is Gary?   _____

20) How old will John be when Gary is 14?   _____

Score [   ] Percentage [%]

Verbal Activity Test 14

Underline the pair of words that are most similar in meaning.

e.g.	track, path	road, river	path, rail
1)	wet, dry	finish, end	brief, long
2)	small, tiny	story, letter	black, blue
3)	walk, run	thin, slim	high, sky

The first six letters of the alphabet are **A B C D E F**. Underline the only word in each line that uses one or more of these letters.

e.g.	moon	toys	day	run	zoo
4)	rotting	young	worry	cane	hot
5)	sorry	rout	hoot	poor	rain
6)	rung	delay	joy	king	lung

Underline the word whose letters are in alphabetical order.

e.g.	rain	man	host	yellow	trap
7)	grey	annoy	colour	able	true
8)	false	bond	fly	pane	tea
9)	try	teach	class	day	mop

Underline the pair of words that are most opposite in meaning.

e.g.	book, comic	night, day	sound, aloud
10)	wild, cross	true, real	under, over
11)	full, empty	cup, mug	cook, bake
12)	animal, bird	knife, cut	past, future

 ae

Underline the word in the brackets that will complete the analogy.

e.g. **Plane** is to **air** as **boat** is to (land, <u>water</u>, pilot)

13) **Pig** is to **trotter** as **leopard** is to (paw, foot, hoof)

14) **Croak** is to **frog** as **cluck** is to (eagle, raven, hen)

15) **In** is to **out** as **come** is to (go, run, arrive)

Study how the second set of letters has been formed from the first, then repeat the process to find the answer. Use the alphabet above to help you.

e.g. **EP**   is to **FQ**   as **GR**   is to <u>HS</u>

16) **DCB** is to **HGF** as **PON** is to _____

17) **BD**   is to **XZ**   as **EG**   is to _____

18) **JK**   is to **LM**   as **QR**   is to _____

Read the following statements and then answer the questions.

Some children use different colours to paint a picture.
Andrew and Mary use yellow paint. Derek and Ellie use green paint. Andrew and Ellie also use blue paint. Derek and Mary use red paint.

(Clue: draw up a table)

e.g. Who uses green and red paint?   <u>Derek</u>

19) Who uses green and blue paint?   _____

20) Who uses yellow and red paint?   _____

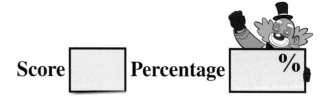

Score [   ] Percentage [%]

Verbal Activity Test 15

Underline the word in the brackets which is most opposite in meaning to the word in capital letters.

e.g. **RIGHT** (true, <u>wrong</u>, correct, bad, real)

1) **ILL** (sick, well, drug, hospital, doctor)

2) **BOIL** (heat, cold, freeze, hot, burn)

3) **MAD** (make, fit, health, sane, pill)

Rearrange the letters in capitals into a proper word so the sentence makes sense.

e.g. Our dog RAKBS loudly. <u>BARKS</u>

4) Melissa was excited about going to the YRATP. _____

5) In January it is usually very OLDC. _____

6) NHEW are you flying to Spain? _____

Choose the correct grouping for each of the words below. Write the group letter in the spaces provided.

A: Mammals   B: Reptiles   C: Birds

e.g. a) robin: <u>C</u>   b) lizard: <u>B</u>

7) a) weasel: ____   b) kite: ____

8) a) crocodile: ____   b) thrush: ____

9) a) beaver: ____   b) snake: ____

Underline the word in the brackets which goes best with the words outside the brackets.

e.g. gerbil, mouse, hamster   (badger, fox, <u>rat</u>, rabbit, beaver)

10) teacher, pupil, classroom   (pool, desk, pitch, roof, ball)

11) bus, train, coach   (chair, passenger, aeroplane, ticket, luggage)

12) table, chair, cupboard   (sofa, kitchen, house, garden, light)

Underline the two words that need to change places in order for the sentence to make sense.

e.g. The mobile <u>rang</u> <u>phone</u> continuously.

13) Make sure the tea has boiled before you make the kettle.

14) The market was closed off for street day.

15) The storm was blown over during the tree.

Underline the four-letter word that is hidden at the end of one word and the beginning of the next word and write it in the space provided. The order of the letters must not be changed.

e.g. My radio can b<u>e ver</u>y loud at times.   _*ever*_

16) The family went to the beach at ten o'clock.   _____

17) The baby was born earlier than expected.   _____

18) The guest arrived at the hotel on Friday.   _____

Read the following statements then answer the questions.
Kay is in the chess club which meets on Tuesday and Thursday.
She is also in the drama club which meets on Wednesday.
On Monday and Tuesday Kay has guitar lessons.

(Clue: draw up a table)

e.g. What activity does Kay only do once a week? ___*drama*___

19) On what school day does Kay not have any
activites?   _____

20) On what day does Kay have two activites?   _____

Score [   ] Percentage [%]

Verbal Activity Test 16

Turn the first word into the last word by changing one letter at a time and making a new word in the middle.

e.g. DAM (DAY) PAY

1) PEW (_____) POT

2) MAN (_____) PUN

3) DID (_____) ADD

Underline one word from each set of brackets that go together to form a compound word. The word in the first set of brackets always comes first.

e.g. (sit, <u>man</u>, stand) (now, <u>age</u>, past)

4) (step, stair, hall) (off, case, pipe)

5) (paint, brush, picture) (colour, draw, box)

6) (bag, music, song) (shopping, pipes, drum)

Write the next word in this pattern of words.

e.g. fan, fun ran, run ban, bun

7) sand, sad band, bad hand, _____

8) pill, spill car, scar lung, _____

9) remember, member relay, lay remain, _____

Write the letter that will end the first word and start the second word in the space provided.

e.g. DIS (H) OUR

10) ME (___) WO

11) BU (____) ES

12) TO (____) LF

If **MDAS** is written in code as **1234**, what words do the following codes represent?

e.g. **232** _DAD_

13) **132** _____

14) **322** _____

15) **344** _____

Write the next letter or letters in the series.

e.g. **AZ**   **BY**   **CX**   **DW**   _EV_

16) **A**   **D**   **G**   **J**   **M**   _____

17) **ZD**   **YE**   **XF**   **WG**   _____

18) **AF**   **CD**   **EB**   **GZ**   _____

Read the following statements and then answer the questions.

Patrick is smaller than Kevin and Kevin is smaller than Larry. Tim is bigger than Kevin but smaller than Larry.

(Clue: use a diagram to help you)

e.g. Who is the smallest?   _Patrick_

19) Who is second biggest?   _____

20) Who is third biggest?   _____

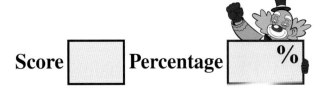

Score [   ] **Percentage** [   ] **%**

Verbal Activity Test 17

Remove one letter from the word in capitals to make a new word. Use the clue to help you.

e.g.	**BLACK**	the opposite of front	_back_
1)	**NESTS**	fishermen use these	_____
2)	**SHOOT**	a bird makes this noise	_____
3)	**TRACE**	you can run in one of these	_____

Use the alphabet above to help you with these questions.

e.g. Which letter is as many places before **T** as **J** is before **M**? _Q_

4) Make a word from the **1st, 16th, 9th** and **14th** letters. _____

5) Which letter is as many places from the beginning of the alphabet as **V** is from the end? ____

6) Which letter is as many places after **K** as **G** is after **B**? ____

Underline the word in the brackets which is most similar in meaning to the word in capital letters.

e.g.	**DIRTY**	(clean, shabby, <u>filthy</u>, clear, sparkling)
7)	**RULER**	(metre, king, crown, control, servant)
8)	**CROSS**	(angry, multiply, frown, kind, loving)
9)	**CLEVER**	(school, teach, able, learn, book)

Underline the word that cannot be made by using the letters of the word in capitals.

e.g.	**POSTER**	rope	stop	rest	<u>star</u>	pore
10)	**SNIPER**	pens	pins	ripe	sing	pier
11)	**HEARTH**	rear	heat	tear	rate	hate
12)	**PLANET**	pale	neat	tame	pane	late

Underline one word in each set of brackets to form the most sensible sentence.

e.g. The (alien, rat, <u>scientist</u>) used the (cheese, <u>magnet</u>, ship) to attract the (tail, <u>metal</u>, boy).

13) My (mother, sister, brother) keeps his (books, socks, football) in the (fridge, wardrobe, oven).

14) The (dog, cat, horse) was (happy, jumped, hungry) and (grunted, mewed, slept) for her food.

15) The (sky, river, horse) was (flowing, dropping, jumping) under the (table, bridge, shop).

Underline the word in the brackets which is most opposite in meaning to the word in capital letters.

e.g. **RIGHT**   (true, <u>wrong</u>, correct, bad, real)

16) **SOFT**   (smooth, hard, tough, fur, rock)

17) **ARRIVE**   (bring, last, leave, come, travel)

18) **WIDE**   (big, bottom, top, small, narrow)

Read the following statements then answer the questions.

Serena and Cora like chips. Cora and Abigail like pizza.
Pat and Serena put mayonnaise on their food.
Abigail and Pat put ketchup on their food.

(Clue: draw up a table)

e.g. Who puts mayonnaise on their chips?   <u>Serena</u>

19) Who puts ketchup on their pizza?   _____

20) Who puts mayonnaise and ketchup on their food?   _____

Score ☐ Percentage ☐ %

Verbal Activity Test 18

Underline the pair of words that are most opposite in meaning.

e.g. book, comic   <u>night, day</u>   sound, aloud

1) bake, bread   neat, untidy   food, eat

2) middle, centre   lift, drop   run, leap

3) wet, dust   outside, airy   dry, moist

Write the same letter, in the spaces provided, which begins all of the words.

e.g. _S_ ink   _S_ ting   _S_ mall   _S_ ale   _S_ port

4) __an   __late   __op   __lane   __rod

5) __lad   __rip   __un   __low   __reen

6) __ail   __mell   __ky   __kin   __cale

Write the next letter or letters in the series.

e.g. **AZ**   **BY**   **CX**   **DW**   <u>EV</u>

7) **FG**   **JK**   **NO**   **RS**   ____

8) **DX**   **FV**   **HT**   **JR**   **LP**   ____

9) **D**   **E**   **G**   **J**   **N**   ____

If **TRADING** is written in code as **7654321**, what words do the following codes represent?

e.g. **6321** <u>RING</u>

10) **6534** _____

11) **46532** _____

12) **16324** _____

Write the letter that will end the first word and start the second word in the space provided.

e.g. DIS (H) OUR

13) EN (___) AY

14) SA (___) OU

15) NEX (___) AX

Write the next word in this pattern of words.

e.g. fan, fun	ran, run	ban, _bun_
16) be, being	do, doing	see, _____
17) pink, ink	face, ace	fare, _____
18) dram, dream	chap, cheap	clan, _____

Work out the correct day by using the information given.

e.g. If the 3rd of May is a Wednesday, what
day was the 30th of April?   _____Sunday_____

(Use a calendar like this to help.)	**30th Apr** **Sun**	1st May Mon	2nd May Tues	3rd May Wed

19) If today is Tuesday the 30th of December,
on which day will the new year begin?   _____

20) If yesterday was Friday the 29th of
November, what day will it be on the
2nd of December?   _____

Score [ ] **Percentage** [ ] **%**

Verbal Activity Test 19

Write the word that can be put in front of each of the following words to make new compound words.

e.g. __come   __hind   __fore   __side   _be_

1) __lid   __ball   __sight   __patch   _____

2) __berry   __bird   __mail   __board   _____

3) __father   __stand   __parent   __child   _____

Turn the first word into the last word by changing one letter at a time and making a new word in the middle.

e.g. DAM (_DAY_) PAY

4) BIB (_____) RUB

5) BIN (_____) TON

6) NUT (_____) BUY

Underline the four-letter word that is hidden at the end of one word and the beginning of the next word and write it in the space provided. The order of the letters must not be changed.

e.g. My radio can b<u>e ver</u>y loud at times.   _ever_

7) We stopped at the petrol station for fuel.   _____

8) Paula trained hard for the gymnastics competition.   _____

9) Don had never earned any money for jobs.   _____

Underline the two words that need to change places in order for the sentence to make sense.

e.g. The mobile <u>rang</u> <u>phone</u> continuously.

ABCDEFGHIJKLMNOPQRSTUVWXYZ

10) Belinda needed her use the computer to complete to homework.

11) The houses floated away over the balloon.

12) Yvonne ran down the road to bus the catch.

Rearrange the letters in capitals into a proper word so the sentence makes sense.

e.g. Our dog RAKBS loudly.   <u>BARKS</u>

13) Our cat loves to eat SHIF.   _____

14) Be CIUKQ or you will be late for school.   _____

15) John sat in the most comfortable HIARC.   _____

Underline the word in the brackets that will complete the analogy.

e.g. **Plane** is to **air** as **boat** is to (land, <u>water</u>, pilot)

16) **Up** is to **down** as **float** is to (sink, swim, drown)

17) **Big** is to **little** as **large** is to (small, huge, enormous)

18) **Cut** is to **knife** as **stir** is to (pot, spoon, soup)

Answer the following questions about school times.

e.g. If lunch hour at school begins at 12.15pm, when does it finish?   <u>1.15pm</u>

19) The first lesson is at 9 o'clock in the morning. If it lasts 50 minutes, when does it finish?   _____

20) The last lesson of the day ends at 3.30pm. If it lasts for one hour and a quarter, when did it start?   _____

Score [   ] Percentage [%]

Verbal Activity Test 20

Underline the two words that are the odd ones out.

	e.g.	small	brief	<u>expand</u>	short	<u>big</u>
1)		sob	water	cry	weep	liquid
2)		plate	table	dish	chair	wardrobe
3)		boat	ship	ocean	canoe	sea

Place the following words in alphabetical order by writing **1, 2, 3, 4, 5** in the brackets.

e.g. are (<u>1</u>) cat (<u>3</u>) day (<u>4</u>) elephant (<u>5</u>) bin (<u>2</u>)

4)	dig (__)	day (__)	deaf (__)	dry (__)	dead (__)
5)	tomb (__)	true (__)	team (__)	tray (__)	top (__)
6)	fig (__)	feel (__)	fray (__)	faint (__)	feat (__)

Underline the two words that are made from the same letters.

	e.g.	toe	<u>end</u>	eat	<u>den</u>	ten
7)		ton	tan	not	tin	nut
8)		nun	won	win	mow	now
9)		pit	pot	tap	top	put

Underline the word that cannot be made by using the letters of the word in capitals.

e.g.	**POSTER**	rope	stop	rest	<u>star</u>	pore
10)	**INVENTS**	nine	vine	even	sent	nest
11)	**CUSTARD**	crust	tars	stud	dust	trade
12)	**SWEATER**	tear	rest	wealth	seat	water

A B C D E F G H I J K L M N O P Q R S T U V W X Y Z

Underline one word in each set of brackets to form the most sensible sentence.

e.g. The (alien, rat, <u>scientist</u>) used the (cheese, <u>magnet</u>, ship) to attract the (tail, <u>metal</u>, boy).

13) When are you going to (tidy, lose, join) the (food, mess, door) in your (room, roof, window)?

14) Did you (shout, eat, pay) the (pencils, sweets, coffee) left in the (garden, fire, drawer)?

15) The hamster (slept, exercised, drank) on his (wheel, cage, nest) for a few (days, weeks, minutes) each day.

___

Underline one word from each set of brackets that go together to form a compound word. The word in the first set of brackets always comes first.

e.g. (car, <u>motor</u>, street, wheel)   (lane, path, <u>way</u>, track)

16) (draw, flow, big, fort)   (water, bridge, castle, moat)

17) (real, fair, colour, ghost)   (ground, light, ride, car)

18) (ship, cat, blue, flag)   (sea, purr, boy, pole)

___

Answer the following questions about the alphabet.

e.g. Which season of the year begins with the **1st** letter of the alphabet?   _autumn_

19) Which day of the week begins with the **23rd** letter of the alphabet?   _____

20) Which month of the year begins with the **6th** letter of the alphabet?   _____

Score [ ]   **Percentage** [ ] **%**

Verbal Activity Test 21

Underline the word which would come third if the following words were arranged in alphabetical order.

e.g.	blue	green	red	<u>orange</u>	yellow
1)	whale	dolphin	shark	porpoise	octopus
2)	lounge	bedroom	kitchen	bathroom	conservatory
3)	spade	fork	roller	shears	rake

Write the word that is similar in meaning to the word in capital letters and rhymes with the second word.

e.g.	**DOG**	ground	hound
4)	**ROAD**	beat	_____
5)	**GROCERIES**	rude	_____
6)	**FRIEND**	wait	_____

Add one letter to the word in capitals to make a new word. Use the clue to help you.

e.g.	**LOW**	not fast	SLOW
7)	**LAP**	to give applause	_____
8)	**SIP**	to fall over	_____
9)	**FAIL**	a person who is weak	_____

Write the next letter or letters in the series.

e.g.	**AZ**	**BY**	**CX**	**DW**	EV
10)	**D**	**A**	**X**	**U**	**R**	____

42   © 2011 Stephen Curran **ae**

11) **BC**   **EF**   **IJ**   **NO**   _____

12) **AC**   **EG**   **IK**   **MO**   _____

If **DREAMS** is written in code as **645372**, what words do the following codes represent?

e.g. **736** _MAD_

13) **2557** _____

14) **5342** _____

15) **4536** _____

Write the letter that will end the first word and start the second word in the space provided.

e.g. DIS (_H_) OUR

16) FI (___) EW

17) HAL (___) ISH

18) STOO (___) USK

Read the following statements and then answer the questions.

Four years ago Priyanka received twice as much pocket money as Sandeep did. Sandeep's pocket money goes up by £1 per year. He now gets £5 a week.

e.g. How much did Sandeep receive two years ago?   _£3.00_

19) How much did Priyanka receive four years ago? £ _____

20) How much will Sandeep receive in 3 year's time? £ _____

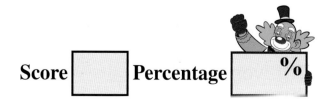

Score [   ] Percentage [   ] %

Verbal Activity Test 22

Write the next word in this pattern of words.

e.g. fan, fun	ran, run	ban, _bun_
1) lint, hint	lost, host	lair, _____
2) got, gut	not, nut	cot, _____
3) mat, met	sat, set	bat, _____

Write the word that can be put in front of each of the following words to make new compound words.

e.g. __come	__hind	__fore	__side	__be__
4) __lamp	__light	__ache	__long	_____
5) __belt	__time	__like	__boat	_____
6) __ship	__field	__axe	__dress	_____

Turn the first word into the last word by changing one letter at a time and making a new word in the middle.

e.g. DAM (_DAY_) PAY

7) FOX (_____) MIX

8) CAT (_____) HAY

9) HUT (_____) LIT

Rewrite these jumbled letters as proper words.

e.g. aogt ___goat___   (Clue: they are
                             all animals)
10) yonp _____

© 2011 Stephen Curran

11) lulb   _____

12) erde   _____

Underline the pair of words that are most opposite in meaning.

e.g. book, comic   <u>night, day</u>   sound, aloud

13) tail, front   long, short   hard, tough

14) shout, whisper   write, pen   see, view

15) sound, sing   over, up   shiny, dull

Underline the word in the brackets that will complete the analogy.

e.g. **Plane** is to **air** as **boat** is to (land, <u>water</u>, pilot)

16) **Train** is to **rails** as **car** is to (garage, road, driver)

17) **Night** is to **day** as **evening** is to (sunrise, morning, afternoon)

18) **Hear** is to **heard** as **see** is to (notice, seen, saw)

Read the following statements and then answer the questions.

Andrew and Martin are tall. John and Pauline are short. Andrew and Pauline have dark hair and Martin and John have fair hair.

(Clue: draw up a table)

e.g. Who is tall with fair hair?   <u>Martin</u>

19) Who is short with dark hair?   _____

20) Who is tall with dark hair?   _____

Score [ ]   Percentage [ ] %

ABCDEFGHIJKLMNOPQRSTUVWXYZ

Verbal Activity Test 23

Underline the two words that are made from the same letters.

e.g. toe <u>end</u> eat <u>den</u> ten

1) mad dim mud may dam

2) row run ran urn nor

3) ton bat too tab ban

Underline the word that cannot be made by using the letters of the word in capitals.

e.g. **POSTER** rope stop rest <u>star</u> pore

4) **WEATHER** wreath hearth hate tree thaw

5) **FRIENDS** dine find fires deaf reins

6) **RELATIONS** notes ration rotate last stone

Underline one word in each set of brackets to form the most sensible sentence.

e.g. The (alien, rat, <u>scientist</u>) used the (cheese, <u>magnet</u>, ship) to attract the (tail, <u>metal</u>, boy).

7) We have a (rug, photograph, curtain) hanging on the (wall, ceiling, floor) in the (fence, hallway, pavement).

8) Peter (bought, scoffed, drank) the (wood, flower, pudding) (quickly, badly, miserably).

9) The (cellist, teacher, fireman) played a (music, solo, duet) in front of the (street, audience, library).

Place the following words in alphabetical order by writing **1**, **2**, **3**, **4**, **5** in the brackets.

e.g. are (1)　　cat (3)　　day (4)　　elephant (5)　 bin (2)

10) meat (__)　 mate (__)　 mean (__)　 moan (__)　 main (__)

11) tray (__)　 train (__)　 tote (__)　 tram (__)　 tame (__)

12) dream (__)　 dry (__)　 drone (__)　 day (__)　 deem (__)

Underline the word in the brackets which is most similar in meaning to the word in capital letters.

e.g. **DIRTY**　　　　(clean, shabby, <u>filthy</u>, clear, sparkling)

13) **TALE**　　　　(book, read, poem, story, moral)

14) **QUICK**　　　　(slow, stop, rapid, move, speed)

15) **THRILL**　　　　(laugh, high, feeling, excite, funny)

Remove one letter from the word in capitals to make a new word. Use the clue to help you.

e.g. **BLACK**　　the opposite of front　　　　_back_

16) **BRINK**　　people skate in this　　　　_____

17) **BLOAT**　　ink can do this　　　　_____

18) **GLOOM**　　used for weaving　　　　_____

Write the next letter or letters in the series.

e.g. **AZ**　　**BY**　　**CX**　　**DW**　　_EV_　　_FU_

19) **C**　　**X**　　**D**　　**Y**　　**E**　　**Z**　　____　 ____

20) **AD**　　**EH**　　**IL**　　**MP**　　____　 ____

Score [　] Percentage [　] %

Verbal Activity Test 24

If **MASTER** is written in code as **ACEGIK**, what words do the following codes represent?

e.g. **KIEG** <u>REST</u>

1) **EGIA** _____

2) **GIKA** _____

3) **EGCK** _____

Write the letter that will end the first word and start the second word in the space provided.

e.g. DIS (<u>H</u>) OUR

4) SON (___) ONE

5) TEN (___) IAL

6) SEA (___) ION

Write the next word in this pattern of words.

e.g. fan, fun   ran, run   ban, <u>bun</u>

7) can, clan   pan, plan   fan, _____

8) feat, heat   four, hour   fang, _____

9) same, some   tame, tome   dame, _____

Underline one word from each set of brackets that go together to form a compound word. The word in the first set of brackets always comes first.

e.g. (car, <u>motor</u>, street, wheel)   (lane, path, <u>way</u>, track)

10) (rat, dog, cat, mice)   (collar, him, lead, her)

A B C D E F G H I J K L M N O P Q R S T U V W X Y Z

11) (big, flag, mat, day)　　　　　　(blue, wood, ship, life)

12) (lamp, light, bulb, glow)　　　　(fence, post, ring, pike)

Turn the first word into the last word by changing one letter at a time and making a new word in the middle.

e.g. DAM (_DAY_) PAY

13) PEN (_____) POT

14) WON (_____) PIN

15) DEN (_____) NEW

Rearrange the letters in capitals into a proper word so the sentence makes sense.

e.g. Our dog RAKBS loudly.　　　　　　　　　BARKS

16) We sit on the HOCUC to watch TV.　　　_____

17) Our cat URSPR when she is happy.　　　_____

18) It is dangerous to throw TOSNES.　　　_____

Underline the two words that are the odd ones out.

e.g. small　　brief　　<u>expand</u>　　short　　<u>big</u>

19) spoon　　cocoa　　tea　　sugar　　coffee

20) road　　street　　bicycle　　motorway　　jeep

Score [　]　**Percentage** [　] %

Verbal Activity Test 25

Underline the word in the brackets that will complete the analogy.

e.g. **Plane** is to **air** as **boat** is to (land, <u>water</u>, pilot)

1) **One** is to **single** as **two** is to (triple, double, three)

2) **Mechanic** is to **car** as **chef** is to (food, waiter, eat)

3) **Ship** is to **port** as **aeroplane** is to (sky, hangar, crash)

Underline the word that cannot be made by using the letters of the word in capitals.

e.g.	**POSTER**	rope	stop	rest	<u>star</u>	pore
4)	**CLOSED**	does	sold	lead	sole	cold
5)	**COMRADE**	rope	come	mode	dear	dram
6)	**BOTTLES**	tote	best	bone	sob	lost

Underline one word in each set of brackets to form the most sensible sentence.

e.g. The (alien, rat, <u>scientist</u>) used the (cheese, <u>magnet</u>, ship) to attract the (tail, <u>metal</u>, boy).

7) Did you (light, eat, wipe) the (table, grass, food) with the (pen, cloth, fur)?

8) The toad (yelled, croaked, screamed) loudly as it (sat, stood, leapt) from the (sky, window, water).

9) The turkey (licked, gobbled, drank) its (meat, flowers, food) (greedily, nicely, quietly).

Underline the word which would come fourth if the following words were arranged in alphabetical order.

e.g. plank   pink   place   priest   <u>point</u>

A B C D E F G H I J K L M N O P Q R S T U V W X Y Z

10)	came	cabin	carrot	cream	cram
11)	follow	fallow	friend	fiend	fall
12)	wing	way	went	whether	want

Underline the two words, one from each set of brackets, that have similar meanings.

e.g. (<u>help</u>, deny, give)　　　　　(true, <u>assist</u>, hurt)

13) (overcast, sunny, black)　　　　(rainy, cloudy, storm)

14) (angry, weary, noisy)　　　　　(silly, funny, tired)

15) (gift, birthday, wrapper)　　　　(buy, special, present)

Add one letter to the word in capitals to make a new word. Use the clue to help you.

e.g. **LOW**　　not fast　　　　　　　　　　SLOW

16) **BAD**　　without hair　　　　　　　_____

17) **MAT**　　part of a ship　　　　　　_____

18) **PLAN**　it grows in the garden　　_____

Read the following statements and then answer the questions about school times.

Paul's first lesson at school is at 9.15am. Each lesson is 30 minutes in length.

e.g. When will the first lesson end?　　　　9.45am

19) Paul has three lessons before break. When does his break start?　　　　_____ am

20) If his break is 15 minutes, when does his fourth lesson end?　　_____

Score ☐ Percentage ☐ %

© 2011 Stephen Curran

Verbal Activity Test 26

Write the next letter or letters in the series.

e.g.	**AZ**	**BY**	**CX**	**DW**	<u>EV</u>	<u>FU</u>
1)	**C**	**D**	**F**	**G**	**I**	___ ___
2)	**W**	**Y**	**A**	**C**	**E**	___ ___
3)	**Z**	**Y**	**W**	**T**		___ ___

Work out which codes belong with which words and then answer the questions.

YES	**SO**	**BOYS**	**YOU**	**RAY**
73	436	417	584	2347

What words do these codes represent?

e.g. **732** <u>SOB</u>

4) **284** _____

5) **1871** _____

6) **7365** _____

Write the letter that will end the first word and start the second word in the space provided.

e.g. DIS (<u>H</u>) OUR

7) AD (___) AY

8) LAS (___) HAN

9) DAM (___) ILOT

Write the next word in this pattern of words.

e.g. fan, fun   ran, run   ban, _bun_

10) dip, grip   beat, great   fin, _____

11) nip, nape   sin, sane   tip, _____

12) cat, date   fat, gate   rat, _____

Underline the word in the brackets that will complete the analogy.

e.g. **Plane** is to **air** as **boat** is to (land, water, pilot)

13) **Boy** is to **girl** as **king** is to (princess, queen, duchess)

14) **Refrigerator** is to **cold** as **oven** is to (warm, burn, hot)

15) **Purchase** is to **sell** as **take** is to (give, snatch, money)

Rewrite these jumbled letters as proper words.

e.g. tar   _art_

16) samht   _____   (Clue: they are all
                                   subjects at school)
17) yrothis   _____

18) ecscein   _____

Read the following statement and then answer the questions.

My watch is five minutes slow and it shows 12.40pm.

e.g. What is the right time now?   _12.45pm_

19) What time did the watch show one hour before? _____

20) If my watch loses 1 minute per hour, what time
     will it show when it is really 5.45pm?   _____

Score [   ] Percentage [   ] %

Verbal Activity Test 27

Write these words in their correct alphabetical order.

e.g.	tea	juice	coffee	chocolate	smoothie
	chocolate	_coffee_	_juice_	_smoothie_	_tea_
1)	rain	hail	snow	drizzle	sleet
	_____	_____	_____	_____	_____
2)	foot	ankle	knee	hand	elbow
	_____	_____	_____	_____	_____
3)	Mercury	Pluto	Saturn	Mars	Neptune
	_____	_____	_____	_____	_____

Underline the two words, one from each set of brackets, that have similar meanings.

e.g. (<u>help</u>, deny, give)   (true, <u>assist</u>, hurt)

4) (peaceful, cross, worry)   (stormy, calm, shout)

5) (cry, stare, smile)   (grin, snarl, puzzle)

6) (ill, health, doctor)   (drug, bandage, sick)

Underline the word that is the odd one out.

e.g.	shirt	<u>thread</u>	blouse	jacket	jersey
7)	kindle	burn	blaze	fire	smoulder
8)	spring	season	summer	winter	autumn
9)	chilly	freezing	wintry	cold	warm

Add one letter to the word in capitals to make a new word. Use the clue to help you.

e.g. **LOW**   not fast   _SLOW_

10) **EAST**   a large amount of food   _____

11) **CAST**   the seashore   _____

12) **LEAN**   we do this at school   _____

If **ORANGES** is written in code as **DAXTUBV**, what words do the following codes represent?

e.g. **AXTU**   _RANG_

13) **TDVB**   _____

14) **DXAV**   _____

15) **UDBV**   _____

Write the letter that will end the first word and start the second word in the space provided.

e.g. DIS (_H_) OUR

16) COR (____) UTY

17) DOW (____) OTE

18) PAI (____) OAR

Read the following statement and then answer the questions about money.

If I had 40p more I would have twice as much as my sister who has 60p.

e.g. How much do I have?   _80p_

19) How much more money does my sister need
to have the same as me?   _____

20) If my sister gives me all she has, how much will
I have then?   £_____

Score [ ] Percentage [ ] %

Verbal Activity Test 28

Write the next word in this pattern of words.

e.g.	fan, fun	ran, run	ban, _bun_		
1)	pit, post	lit, lost	hit, _____		
2)	men, main	pen, pain	gen, _____		
3)	tone, on	lank, an	sink, _____		

Underline one word in each set of brackets to form the most sensible sentence.

e.g. The (alien, rat, <u>scientist</u>) used the (cheese, <u>magnet</u>, ship) to attract the (tail, <u>metal</u>, boy).

4) The (yacht, bus, cabin) was (tossed, sunk, washed) about on the (ocean, beach, pond).

5) The (horses, sheep, dogs) (grunted, neighed, mooed) from within their (kennel, house, stable).

6) Jane (picked, read, grew) her (book, mat, pen) before she went to (the tunnel, bed, carpet).

Underline the word in the brackets that will complete the analogy

e.g. **Plane** is to **air** as **boat** is to (land, <u>water</u>, pilot)

7) **Sun** is to **shine** as **fire** is to (red, glow, day)

8) **Neck** is to **necklace** as **arm** is to (bracelet, ring, beads)

9) **Cow** is to **calf** as **goat** is to (baby, foal, kid)

Underline the word in the brackets which is most opposite in meaning to the word in capital letters.

e.g. **RIGHT** (true, <u>wrong</u>, correct, bad, real)

  ae

10) **CROUCH**   (crawl, leap, balance, slide, lie)

11) **PLAY**   (fun, job, enjoy, work, write)

12) **ROUGH**   (bristle, smooth, liquid, velvet, glue)

Remove one letter from the word in capitals to make a new word. Use the clue to help you.

e.g. **BLACK**   the opposite of front   <u>back</u>

13) **COUCH**   we say this, if it hurts   _____

14) **PINK**   used for writing   _____

15) **PLANE**   part of a window   _____

Write the letter that will end the first word and start the second word in the space provided.

e.g. DIS (<u>H</u>) OUR

16) HIR (____) ND

17) AR (____) ATE

18) FI (____) UBY

If **COMPUTER** is written in code as **12345678**, what are the following words in code?

e.g. **COME** <u>1237</u>

19) **ROOM** _____

20) **MOPE** _____

Score [ ] Percentage [%]

Verbal Activity Test 29

Underline the word in the brackets which is most similar in meaning to the word in capital letters.

e.g. **DIRTY**   (clean, shabby, <u>filthy</u>, clear, sparkling)

1) **TRUCK**   (van, train, car, lorry, tram)

2) **SOUND**   (hear, listen, noise, loud, speaker)

3) **QUARREL**   (agree, argue, discuss, talk, listen)

Write the next letter or letters in the series.

e.g. **AZ**   **BY**   **CX**   **DW**   <u>EV</u>   <u>FU</u>

4) **A**   **F**   **J**   **M**   ____   ____

5) **GH**   **KL**   **OP**   **ST**   ____   ____

6) **AG**   **BF**   **CE**   **DD**   ____   ____

Underline the word that is the odd one out.

e.g. shirt   <u>thread</u>   blouse   jacket   jersey

7) chair   bench   stool   ledge   seat

8) pavement   path   hill   track   road

9) join   separate   unite   group   merge

Rewrite these jumbled letters as proper words.

e.g. teshol   <u>hostel</u>

10) etnt   _____

11) letoh   _____

(Clue: they are all places you can stay in on holiday)

12) racavna   _____

© 2011 Stephen Curran

Write the same letter, in the spaces provided, which begins all of the words.

e.g. _S_ ink   _S_ ting   _S_ mall   _S_ ale   _S_ port

13) ___ish   ___aste   ___et   ___ash   ___eb

14) ___at   ___ang   ___ounce   ___link   ___oy

15) ___ond   ___ie   ___in   ___at   ___ay

Work out which codes belong with which words and then answer the questions.

SEA	SAD	DEAR	DARE	DO
46	4125	312	324	4251

What words do these codes represent?

e.g. **5124** READ

16) **4665** _____

17) **24415** _____

18) **56313** _____

Read the following statements and then answer the questions. Janice and Tom like pasta. Tom and Gurpreet like salad. Gurpreet and Janice like curry. Only Tom does not like pizza.

(Clue: draw up a table)

e.g. Who likes pizza and pasta?   Janice

19) Who likes everything but pasta?   _____

20) Who does not like salad?   _____

Score [ ] **Percentage** [ ] **%**

Verbal Activity Test 30

Write the next word in this pattern of words.

e.g. fan, fun	ran, run	ban, _bun_
1) rim, rind	bar, band	fib, _____
2) goat, go	toad, to	soot, _____
3) bell, balls	cell, calls	hell, _____

Underline the two words that are most opposite in meaning.

e.g. <u>tall</u>	small	<u>short</u>	tiny	fat
4) cheap	buy	expensive	diamond	wealth
5) misty	dark	heavy	glass	clear
6) top	mountain	down	valley	sea

Add one letter to the word in capitals to make a new word. Use the clue to help you.

e.g. **LOW**	not fast	_SLOW_
7) **FEET**	a group of ships	_____
8) **FOR**	a garden tool	_____
9) **BEAK**	to damage something	_____

Underline the word in the brackets which is most similar in meaning to the word in capital letters.

e.g. **DIRTY**   (clean, shabby, <u>filthy</u>, clear, sparkling)

10) **FOREVER**   (never, sometimes, always, time, end)

11) **STREAM**   (sand, sea, brook, waterfall, pool)

12) **CRATE**   (luggage, barrel, vat, bag, box)

If **TRANCE** is written in code as **246897**, what words do the following codes represent?

e.g. **964**   _CAR_

13) **4697**   _____

14) **2764**   _____

15) **8762**   _____

Study how the second set of letters has been formed from the first, then repeat the process to find the answer. Use the alphabet above to help you.

e.g. **EP**   is to **FQ**   as **GR**   is to _HS_

16) **ZX**   is to **WU**   as **PN**   is to ____

17) **BZ**   is to **DX**   as **RW**   is to ____

18) **ACE**   is to **FHJ**   as **PRT** is to ____

Underline one word in each set of brackets to form the most sensible sentence.

e.g. The (alien, rat, <u>scientist</u>) used the (cheese, <u>magnet</u>, ship) to attract the (tail, <u>metal</u>, boy).

19) The (woman, girl, child) rode his (bicycle, car, motorcycle) to (garage, school, home).

20) A (chilly, clean, dirty) wind (ran, blew, grew) across the (plain, day, week).

Score [   ] Percentage [%]

Verbal Activity Test 31

Underline the word that needs to be changed in order for the sentence to make sense. Write the new word that should replace it in the space provided.

e.g. I felt so ill I went to the <u>clown</u>.   *doctor*

1) I thirstily grew some juice in the cafe.   _____

2) Joshua flew his bicycle to school.   _____

3) Daisy put a date on the envelope and posted it.   _____

Write the letter that will end the first word and start the second word in the space provided.

e.g. DIS (H) OUR

4) DEN (____) URN

5) MEA (____) OAN

6) BUF (____) AIR

Remove one letter from the word in capitals to make a new word. Use the clue to help you.

e.g. **BLACK**   the opposite of front   *back*

7) **STING**   a pop star can do this   _____

8) **CLOCK**   you need a key for this   _____

9) **SHARP**   a musical instrument   _____

Underline the two words that are most opposite in meaning.

e.g. <u>tall</u>   small   <u>short</u>   tiny   fat

10) joy   great   hurt   sorrow   life

11) ball   catch   cricket   throw   run

12) play   score   defend   goal   attack

If **BREADS** is written in code as **123456**, find the following codes and words.

e.g. **545**   DAD

13) **235** _____

14) **BEAR** _____

15) **134256** _____

Underline the word in the brackets that will complete the analogy.

e.g. **Plane** is to **air** as **boat** is to (land, <u>water</u>, pilot)

16) **Fish** is to **sea** as **flower** is to (petal, ground, water)

17) **Car** is to **garage** as **ship** is to (sail, sea, harbour)

18) **July** is to **May** as **November** is to (August, September, December)

Write the next letter or letters in the series.

e.g. **AZ**   **BY**   **CX**   **DW**   <u>EV</u>   <u>FU</u>

19) **DG**   **IL**   **NQ**   **SV**   ____   ____

20) **AT**   **BR**   **CP**   **DN**   ____   ____

Score ☐ Percentage ☐ %

Verbal Activity Test 32

Underline the pair of words that are most similar in meaning.

e.g. <u>track, path</u>   road, river   path, rail

1) coffee, tea   sand, rock   break, smash

2) sad, sorry   laugh, chuckle   hard, soft

3) well, sick   aged, old   good, bad

Underline one word in each set of brackets to form the most sensible sentence.

e.g. The (alien, rat, <u>scientist</u>) used the (cheese, <u>magnet</u>, ship) to attract the (tail, <u>metal</u>, boy).

4) Did you (ever, try, return) swim in the (lake, pond, sea) with (ship, dolphins, ocean)?

5) The (cloud, sea, crabs) was (crashing, living, rushing) on the (floor, shore, door).

6) My (cat, horse, doll) is wearing a (solid, pretty, plate) (fur, hair, dress).

Underline the word in the brackets that will complete the analogy.

e.g. **Plane** is to **air** as **boat** is to (land, <u>water</u>, pilot)

7) **Bright** is to **dim** as **front** is to (spine, back, first)

8) **Moan** is to **mean** as **loan** is to (lane, lead, lean)

9) **Nose** is to **smell** as **tongue** is to (food, taste, sweet)

Place the following words in alphabetical order by writing **1, 2, 3, 4, 5** in the brackets.

e.g. are (<u>1</u>)   cat (<u>3</u>)   day (<u>4</u>)   elephant (<u>5</u>) bin (<u>2</u>)

10) feel (__)   farm (__)   form (__)   full (__)   figs (__)

11) trap (__)   top (__)   train (__)   toy (__)   tap (__)

12) long (__)   lone (__)   loop (__)   lute (__)   late (__)

Add one letter to the word in capitals to make a new word. Use the clue to help you.

e.g. **LOW**   not fast   _SLOW_

13) **BIND**   without sight   _____

14) **RAVE**   a big black bird   _____

15) **NOT**   a musical sound   _____

Write the letter that will end the first word and start the second word in the space provided.

e.g. DIS (_H_) OUR

16) PLA (___) ICE

17) SPLI (___) RIP

18) SEE (___) RIP

Answer the following questions about children's ages.

e.g. Jason is three quarters the age of Kelly.
Jason is 9. How old is Kelly?   _12_

19) In 4 years' time Simon will be twice as old as I am now. If I am 8, how old is Simon?   _____

20) If Rajan was a year older he would be three times as old as his cousin Bilal. If Bilal is 3, how old is Rajan?   _____

Score [   ]   Percentage [   ] %

A B C D E F G H I J K L M N O P Q R S T U V W X Y Z

Verbal Activity Test 33

Underline the word that needs to be changed in order for the sentence to make sense. Write the new word that should replace it in the space provided.

e.g. I felt so ill I went to the <u>clown</u>. *doctor*

1) The cat wagged his tail when his owner took him for a walk. _____

2) Mother asks me to destroy my bed each morning before I leave for school. _____

3) It was a cold day so we lit the table to keep warm. _____

Write the letter that will end the first word and start the second word in the space provided.

e.g. DIS (H) OUR

4) FAL (___) AWN

5) TRE (___) VEN

6) FOO (___) HEN

Write the same letter, in the spaces provided, which begins all of the words.

e.g. _S_ink   _S_ting   _S_mall   _S_ale   _S_port

7) __ole   __ouse   __eat   __ard   __ear

8) __ool   __lag   __lower   __ig   __og

9) __ill   __late   __uff   __ony   __in

Underline the two words that are most opposite in meaning.

e.g. <u>tall</u>   small   <u>short</u>   tiny   fat

© 2011 Stephen Curran

A B C D E F G H I J K L M N O P Q R S T U V W X Y Z

10)	laugh	tears	giggle	cry	jeer
11)	eat	feast	hungry	famine	food
12)	thought	memory	remember	lost	forget

Underline the word in the brackets that will complete the analogy.

e.g. **Plane** is to **air** as **boat** is to (land, <u>water</u>, pilot)

13) **Horse** is to **gallop** as **wallaby** is to (hop, run, trot)

14) **Ice** is to **slippery** as **glue** is to (join, sticky, cement)

15) **Swan** is to **cygnet** as **frog** is to (baby, tadpole, fish)

Remove one letter from the word in capitals to make a new word. Use the clue to help you.

e.g. **BLACK**   the opposite of front   <u>back</u>

16) **FEAR**   not close   _____

17) **LEAST**   opposite of first   _____

18) **RAGE**   an old cloth   _____

Work out the correct day by using the information given.

e.g. If the 3rd of May is a Wednesday, what day was the 30th of April?   <u>Sunday</u>

(Use a calendar like this to help.)	**30th Apr**	1st May	2nd May	3rd May
	Sun	Mon	Tues	Wed

19) If the 3rd of October is a Tuesday, what day was the 29th of September?   _____

20) If the 30th of June is a Sunday, what day will it be on the 4th of July?   _____

Score [ ]   Percentage [ ] %

Verbal Activity Test 34

Underline the two words that are most similar in meaning.

e.g. <u>new</u>   old   shiny   <u>fresh</u>   dead

1) broad   slow   small   wide   large

2) buy   prison   burgle   police   steal

3) absent   tick   away   present   note

Underline one word in each set of brackets to form the most sensible sentence.

e.g. The (alien, rat, <u>scientist</u>) used the (cheese, <u>magnet</u>, ship) to attract the (tail, <u>metal</u>, boy).

4) Robert (leapt, squeezed, hopped) under the (road, grass, fence) as (sadly, lazily, quickly) as he could.

5) Jagjit (wished, watched, jumped) the (damp, colourful, sparkle) display of (bonfire, raining, fireworks).

6) Radhika's (leg, hand, foot) would not (fit, size, fill) into the (hat, shoe, coat).

Underline the word that needs to be changed in order for the sentence to make sense. Write the new word that should replace it in the space provided.

e.g. I felt so ill I went to the <u>clown</u>.   _doctor_

7) On my way home from school I was completely soaked by the wardrobe.   _____

8) The jumbo jet sailed over mountain tops.   _____

9) After meals you should hammer your teeth.   _____

Write the letter that will end the first word and start the second word in the space provided.

e.g. DIS (_H_) OUR

10) CAR (___) IVE

11) LI (___) ET

12) REN (___) EA

Underline the word in the brackets that will complete the analogy.

e.g. **Plane** is to **air** as **boat** is to (land, <u>water</u>, pilot)

13) **Note** is to **tone** as **tare** is to (rota, rate, rats)

14) **Zebra** is to **stripes** as **leopard** is to (yellow, fur, spots)

15) **Dog** is to **bite** as **hen** is to (peck, chew, gobble)

Add one letter to the word in capitals to make a new word. Use the clue to help you.

e.g. **LOW** not fast SLOW

16) **LATE** we use this at meal times _____

17) **NET** birds live in this _____

18) **RIGHT** to have a scare _____

Read the following statements and then answer the questions.
Marion and Yasib like soup. Roberta and Mark like rice.
Mark and Marion like lasagne. Yasib and Roberta like chips.

(Clue: draw up a table)

e.g. Who likes rice and lasagne? Mark

19) Who likes soup and lasagne? _____

20) Who likes rice and chips? _____

Score [ ] Percentage [ ] %

Verbal Activity Test 35

Write the next word in this pattern of words.

e.g. fan, fun	ran, run	ban, _bun_
1) run, rang	bun, bang	fun, _____
2) pot, pate	dot, date	got, _____
3) pail, pale	mail, male	bail, _____

Write the word that is similar in meaning to the word in capital letters and rhymes with the second word.

e.g. **DOG**	ground	_hound_
4) **VEHICLE**	pram	_____
5) **MIDDAY**	spoon	_____
6) **BOX**	date	_____

Work out which codes belong with which words and then answer the questions.

DOVE	WET	WANT	DOT
975	4687	465	9325

What words do these codes represent?

e.g. **465** _DOT_

7) **5627** _____

8) **8725** _____

9) **73572** _____

Write the letter that will end the first word and start the second word in the space provided.

e.g. DIS (_H_) OUR

10) FIRS (____) ON

11) BAT (____) ARM

12) THE (____) ANY

Underline one word in each set of brackets to form the most sensible sentence.

e.g. The (alien, rat, <u>scientist</u>) used the (cheese, <u>magnet</u>, ship) to attract the (tail, <u>metal</u>, boy).

13) The (birds, insects, flowers) needed (washing, watering drowning) as they were very (dry, cold, wet).

14) There is a (cold, slimy, clammy) wind (hooting, blowing, glowing) (inside, under, outside).

15) The (snake, swimmer, ship) (dived, fished, played) into the (net, bath, pool).

Remove one letter from the word in capitals to make a new word. Use the clue to help you.

e.g. **BLACK**   the opposite of front   <u>back</u>

16) **BOWL**   part of a ship   _____

17) **BOAT**   a mammal   _____

18) **FINE**   part of a fish   _____

Write the next letter or letters in the series.

e.g. **AZ**   **BY**   **CX**   **DW**   <u>EV</u>   <u>FU</u>

19) **D**   **I**   **M**   **P**   ____   ____

20) **P**   **S**   **U**   **X**   **Z**   ____   ____

Score [ ] Percentage [ ] %

Verbal Activity Test 36

Write the same letter, in the spaces provided, which begins all of the words.

e.g. _S_ ink   _S_ ting   _S_ mall   _S_ ale   _S_ port

1) __ase   __lean   __heap   __row   __all

2) __able   __ray   __an   __hen   __oy

3) __ind   __ould   __hale   __ater   __as

Underline the two words that are most similar in meaning.

e.g. <u>new</u>   old   shiny   <u>fresh</u>   dead

4) shape   circular   square   round   ball

5) roam   run   lost   wander   jump

6) loud   scream   talk   tell   shriek

Underline the word in the brackets that will complete the analogy.

e.g. **Plane** is to **air** as **boat** is to (land, <u>water</u>, pilot)

7) **Player** is to **team** as **sailor** is to (ship, group, crew)

8) **Laugh** is to **cry** as **bless** is to (pray, curse, hurt)

9) **Hammer** is to **nail** as **spanner** is to (screw, pin, nut)

Write the letter that will end the first word and start the second word in the space provided.

e.g. DIS (_H_) OUR

10) REE (___) ALL

11) YOU (___) OB

12) SE (___) AND

    © 2011 Stephen Curran

Underline the two words that are most opposite in meaning.

e.g.	<u>tall</u>	small	<u>short</u>	tiny	fat
13)	exit	inside	leave	sign	entrance
14)	replace	break	remove	relay	drop
15)	day	noon	dawn	light	dusk

Work out which codes belong with which words and then answer the questions.

JOY	**TOO**	**JOKE**	**BONE**
3479	**5429**	**844**	**346**

What words do these codes represent?

e.g. **346** _JOY_

16) **7992** _____

17) **2942** _____

18) **84792** _____

Read the following statements and then answer the questions.

Four children buy sweets at their local shop. Andrea and Ellie buy chocolate. David and Ellie buy lollipops. Andrea and Michael buy chews. David and Michael buy toffee.

(Clue: draw up a table)

e.g. Who buys chocolate and lollipops? _Ellie_

19) Who does not buy toffee or lollipops? _____

20) Which two people buy toffee? _____ _____

Score ☐ Percentage ☐ %

ae © 2011 Stephen Curran

Answers

Test 1

1) Where is the toilet?
2) It costs four pounds.
3) Change into your best clothes.
4) 712
5) 517
6) 512
7) patch
8) glad
9) scowl
10) fish
11) rise
12) stable
13) had
14) can
15) sins
16) shoes & sandals
17) edge & rear
18) treat & else
19) Paul
20) John

Test 2

1) late
2) mate
3) edit
4) rail
5) pain
6) hunt
7) tan & ant
8) pat & tap
9) nib & bin
10) go
11) vet
12) rut
13) false
14) false
15) true
16) bawl & ball
17) their & there

18) sail & sale
19) Bobby
20) 3

Test 3

1) k
2) e
3) d
4) days
5) den
6) paws
7) jeans
8) belt
9) shirt
10) bus car coach lorry moped
11) cricket football netball rounders tennis
12) bedroom hall kitchen loft lounge
13) hand
14) read
15) drag
16) plan
17) tone
18) term
19) Deena
20) Ella

Test 4

1) drops
2) wrote
3) later
4) bard
5) tops
6) live
7) lower
8) lease
9) rain
10) far & near
11) light & dark
12) love & hate
13) Prianka read her history book.

Answers

14) Clean your shoes for school.
15) John walked up the steep hill.
16) ten & net
17) rat & tar
18) act & cat
19) 7
20) 11

Test 5

1) faces
2) fuel
3) players
4) MN
5) NL
6) QS
7) bud
8) fat
9) bead
10) cat
11) drink
12) April
13) cosks : socks
14) soer : rose
15) owls : slow
16) bear & bare
17) meat & meet
18) heel & heal
19) Gail
20) Carol

Test 6

1) gas & sag
2) ate & tea
3) tow & two
4) pear
5) rein
6) reed
7) 2
8) a
9) 1
10) flow

11) snap
12) rats
13) 634
14) 563
15) TOWN
16) n
17) e
18) i
19) Monday
20) Saturday

Test 7

1) oak
2) birch
3) yew
4) owl
5) van
6) cub
7) near
8) pal
9) soot
10) dog
11) narrow
12) lead
13) O
14) IR
15) VU
16) hear & here
17) knew & new
18) by & buy
19) Adam
20) Cynthia

Test 8

1) He arrived home very early.
2) Where is your school homework?
3) We took the train to London.
4) plumage
5) sett
6) dates
7) a

Answers

8) l & n
9) s
10) hit
11) lop
12) evil
13) 4
14) 5
15) 5
16) tram
17) coach
18) ferry
19) Monday
20) Tuesday

Test 9
1) see & sea
2) rows & rose
3) some & sum
4) 4332
5) staff
6) rate
7) HAT
8) TON
9) FAN
10) begin & start
11) hit & strike
12) earth & land
13) night
14) lame
15) worse
16) open & shut
17) buy & sell
18) live & die
19) 17
20) 24

Test 10
1) nest
2) pages
3) wet

4) It is dangerous to climb trees.
5) Children like to receive Christmas presents.
6) We spent our holiday in Spain.
7) pop
8) fen
9) tells
10) a & u
11) i
12) e
13) psaws : wasps
14) shca : cash
15) fche : chef
16) right & wrong
17) soft & hard
18) loud & quiet
19) Naomi
20) Priya

Test 11
1) tub & but
2) ram & arm
3) arc & car
4) 4, 3, 1, 5, 2
5) 3, 1, 5, 4, 2
6) 3, 5, 1, 2, 4
7) stem & nectar
8) jug & bowl
9) room & kitchen
10) blue
11) rope
12) stop
13) I
14) UT
15) GE
16) wild
17) feeble
18) found

19) Jane
20) Roy

Test 12
1) BOOK
2) BIKE
3) HOOK
4) a) C   b) B
5) a) B   b) A
6) a) A   b) C
7) cuckoo
8) rules
9) chapter
10) final & goal
11) harness & dog
12) cold & toes
13) wasp
14) wear
15) beat
16) sea & gull
17) jaw & bone
18) cross & roads
19) 4th June
20) Sunday

Test 13
1) pot
2) sing
3) mane
4) T
5) P
6) L
7) 246
8) bait
9) 2432
10) sand
11) bat
12) bear
13) metal
14) shelf

Answers

15) period
16) bread
17) shops
18) roots
19) 8
20) 10

Test 14
1) finish, end
2) small, tiny
3) thin, slim
4) cane
5) rain
6) delay
7) annoy
8) fly
9) mop
10) under, over
11) full, empty
12) past, future
13) paw
14) hen
15) go
16) TSR
17) AC
18) ST
19) Ellie
20) Mary

Test 15
1) well
2) freeze
3) sane
4) party
5) cold
6) when
7) a) A b) C
8) a) B b) C
9) a) A b) B
10) desk

11) aeroplane
12) sofa
13) tea & kettle
14) market & street
15) storm & tree
16) chat
17) near
18) star
19) Friday
20) Tuesday

Test 16
1) PET
2) PAN
3) AID
4) stair & case
5) paint & box
6) bag & pipes
7) had
8) slung
9) main
10) T
11) Y
12) E
13) MAD
14) ADD
15) ASS
16) P
17) VH
18) IX
19) Tim
20) Kevin

Test 17
1) NETS
2) HOOT
3) RACE
4) PAIN
5) E
6) P

7) king
8) angry
9) able
10) sing
11) rear
12) tame
13) brother, socks, wardrobe
14) cat, hungry, mewed
15) river, flowing, bridge
16) hard
17) leave
18) narrow
19) Abigail
20) Pat

Test 18
1) neat, untidy
2) lift, drop
3) dry, moist
4) p
5) g
6) s
7) VW
8) NN
9) S
10) RAID
11) DRAIN
12) GRIND
13) D
14) Y
15) T
16) seeing
17) are
18) clean
19) Thursday
20) Monday

Test 19
1) eye
2) black

            ae

Answers

3) grand
4) RIB
5) TIN
6) BUT
7) west
8) fort
9) rear
10) her & to
11) houses & balloon
12) bus & catch
13) FISH
14) QUICK
15) CHAIR
16) sink
17) small
18) spoon
19) 9.50am
20) 2.15pm

Test 20
1) water & liquid
2) dish & plate
3) ocean & sea
4) 4, 1, 3, 5, 2
5) 2, 5, 1, 4, 3
6) 4, 3, 5, 1, 2
7) ton & not
8) won & now
9) pot & top
10) even
11) trade
12) wealth
13) tidy, mess, room
14) eat, sweets, drawer
15) exercised, wheel, minutes
16) draw & bridge
17) fair & ground
18) flag & pole
19) Wednesday
20) February

Test 21
1) porpoise
2) conservatory
3) roller
4) STREET
5) FOOD
6) MATE
7) CLAP
8) SLIP
9) FRAIL
10) O
11) TU
12) QS
13) SEEM
14) EARS
15) READ
16) N
17) F
18) D
19) £2.00
20) £8.00

Test 22
1) hair
2) cut
3) bet
4) head
5) life
6) battle
7) FIX
8) HAT
9) HIT
10) pony
11) bull
12) deer
13) long, short
14) shout, whisper
15) shiny, dull
16) road
17) morning

18) saw
19) Pauline
20) Andrew

Test 23
1) mad & dam
2) run & urn
3) bat & tab
4) hearth
5) deaf
6) rotate
7) photograph, wall, hallway
8) scoffed, pudding, quickly
9) cellist, solo, audience
10) 4, 2, 3, 5, 1
11) 5, 3, 2, 4, 1
12) 3, 5, 4, 1, 2
13) story
14) rapid
15) excite
16) RINK
17) BLOT
18) LOOM
19) F, A
20) QT, UX

Test 24
1) STEM
2) TERM
3) STAR
4) G
5) D
6) L
7) flan
8) hang
9) dome
10) rat & her
11) flag & ship
12) lamp & post
13) PET

Answers

14) WIN
15) DEW
16) COUCH
17) PURRS
18) STONES
19) spoon & sugar
20) bicycle & jeep

Test 25
1) double
2) food
3) hangar
4) lead
5) rope
6) bone
7) wipe, table, cloth
8) croaked, leapt, water
9) gobbled, food, greedily
10) cram
11) follow
12) whether
13) overcast & cloudy
14) weary & tired
15) gift & present
16) BALD
17) MAST
18) PLANT
19) 10.45am
20) 11.30am

Test 26
1) J, L
2) G, I
3) P, K
4) BAY
5) EASE
6) SOUR
7) D
8) T
9) P

10) grin
11) tape
12) sate
13) queen
14) hot
15) give
16) maths
17) history
18) science
19) 11.40am
20) 5.35pm

Test 27
1) drizzle, hail, rain, sleet, snow
2) ankle, elbow, foot, hand, knee
3) Mars, Mercury, Neptune, Pluto, Saturn
4) peaceful & calm
5) smile & grin
6) ill & sick
7) fire
8) season
9) warm
10) FEAST
11) COAST
12) LEARN
13) NOSE
14) OARS
15) GOES
16) D
17) N
18) R
19) 20p
20) £1.40

Test 28
1) host
2) gain
3) in
4) yacht, tossed, ocean
5) horses, neighed, stable

6) read, book, bed
7) glow
8) bracelet
9) kid
10) leap
11) work
12) smooth
13) OUCH
14) INK
15) PANE
16) E
17) M
18) R
19) 8223
20) 3247

Test 29
1) lorry
2) noise
3) argue
4) O, P
5) WX, AB
6) EC, FB
7) ledge
8) hill
9) separate
10) tent
11) hotel
12) caravan
13) w
14) b
15) p
16) DOOR
17) ADDER
18) ROSES
19) Gurpreet
20) Janice

Test 30
1) find
2) so

3) halls
4) cheap & expensive
5) misty & clear
6) mountain & valley
7) FLEET
8) FORK
9) BREAK
10) always
11) brook
12) box
13) RACE
14) TEAR
15) NEAT
16) MK
17) TU
18) UWY
19) child, bicycle, school
20) chilly, blew, plain

Test 31
1) grew : drank
2) flew : rode
3) date : stamp
4) T
5) L
6) F
7) SING
8) LOCK
9) HARP
10) joy & sorrow
11) throw & catch
12) attack & defend
13) RED
14) 1342
15) BEARDS
16) ground
17) harbour
18) September
19) XA, CF
20) EL, FJ

Test 32
1) break, smash
2) laugh, chuckle
3) aged, old
4) ever, sea, dolphins
5) sea, crashing, shore
6) doll, pretty, dress
7) back
8) lean
9) taste
10) 2, 1, 4, 5, 3
11) 5, 2, 4, 3, 1
12) 3, 2, 4, 5, 1
13) BLIND
14) RAVEN
15) NOTE
16) N
17) T
18) D
19) 12
20) 8

Test 33
1) cat : dog
2) destroy : make
3) table : fire
4) L
5) E
6) T
7) h
8) f
9) p
10) laugh & cry
11) feast & famine
12) remember & forget
13) hop
14) sticky
15) tadpole
16) FAR
17) LAST
18) RAG

Answers

19) Friday
20) Thursday

Test 34

1) broad & wide
2) burgle & steal
3) absent & away
4) squeezed, fence, quickly
5) watched, colourful, fireworks
6) foot, fit, shoe
7) <u>wardrobe</u> : rain
8) <u>sailed</u> : flew
9) <u>hammer</u> : brush
10) D
11) P
12) T
13) rate
14) spots
15) peck
16) PLATE
17) NEST
18) FRIGHT
19) Marion
20) Roberta

Test 35

1) fang
2) gate
3) bale
4) TRAM
5) NOON
6) CRATE
7) TONE
8) VENT
9) EATEN
10) T

11) H
12) M
13) flowers, watering, dry
14) cold, blowing, outside
15) swimmer, dived, pool
16) BOW
17) BAT
18) FIN
19) R, S
20) C, E

Test 36

1) c
2) t
3) w
4) circular & round
5) roam & wander
6) scream & shriek
7) crew
8) curse
9) nut
10) F
11) R
12) W
13) exit & entrance
14) replace & remove
15) dawn & dusk
16) KEEN
17) NEON
18) TOKEN
19) Andrea
20) David & Michael

PROGRESS CHARTS

Test	Mark	%
1		
2		
3		
4		
5		
6		
7		
8		
9		
10		
11		
12		
13		
14		
15		
16		
17		
18		

Test	Mark	%
19		
20		
21		
22		
23		
24		
25		
26		
27		
28		
29		
30		
31		
32		
33		
34		
35		
36		

CERTIFICATE OF

ACHIEVEMENT

This certifies

_____

has successfully completed

11+ Verbal Activity
Year 3/4
TESTBOOK **1**

Overall percentage
score achieved

%

Comment _____

_____

Signed _____

(teacher/parent/guardian)

Date _____